Planet Emerald

A play by Julia Donaldson
Illustrated by Emma Yarlett

Characters

Miss Green

Alex

Wilfred

Naveed

Rob

Tessa

Miss Green: Good morning, children. I am Miss Green.

Wilfred: Where is Mr Bell, Miss?

Miss Green: Mr Bell is ill today.

Rob: Are you ill too, Miss? You look a bit green.

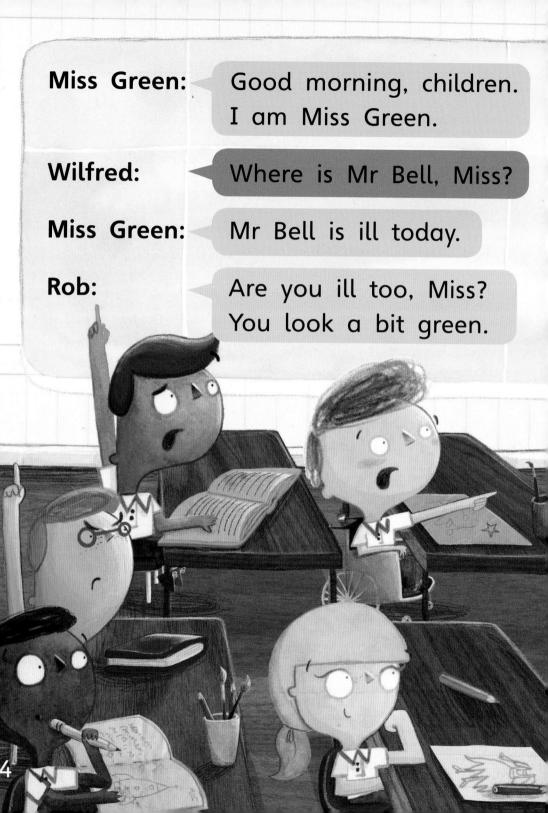

Miss Green: That is because I am from Planet Emerald. Now, let's do some sums. What's three plus three?

5

Tessa: Er ... six, Miss.

Miss Green: No, it's thirty-three.

Alex: But Mr Bell told us it was six.

Miss Green: Well, on Planet Emerald it's thirty-three. What's two plus two?

Naveed: Er ... twenty-two?

Miss Green: No, it's a ballet dress.

Wilfred: How can it be a ballet dress?

Miss Green: Two plus two is tutu. And a tutu is a ballet dress.

Tessa: Yes, it is. My mum made one for me when I was in a show.

Miss Green: Now, let's do some painting!

Rob: Good. I like painting.

Wilfred: So do I!

Miss Green: That's a good painting, Alex. But what is that round thing?

Alex: It's the sun, Miss.

Miss Green: Then why is it yellow?

Alex: Well, the sun is yellow.

Miss Green: No, it's not. It's green. Add a bit of blue to the yellow paint.

Naveed: Do you like my painting, Miss?

Miss Green: Well, I like the green grass. But what's this white thing?

Naveed: It's a sheep.

Miss Green: Then paint it green.

Alex: But sheep are white!

Miss Green: On Planet Emerald, the sheep are green.

Wilfred: Green **sheep**? Is everything on Planet Emerald green?

Miss Green: Yes. The houses are green. The shops are green. So are the cats and dogs.

Rob: Is your car green, Miss?

Miss Green: Look out of the window and you'll see!

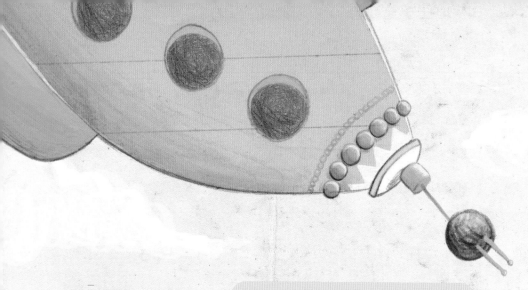

Tessa: That's not a car! That's a rocket!

Miss Green: Yes. Zoom, rocket, zoom!

She clicks her fingers. The rocket zooms in.

Naveed: Wow! Why did you bring the rocket here, Miss?

Miss Green: Because we are all going on a trip to my planet.

Alex: What, now?

Miss Green: Yes! Hop in. There's room for all of us.

They get into the rocket.

Wilfred: Will we get there soon, Miss?

Miss Green: Yes. This is an extra-fast rocket. Hold tight!

Children: Planet Emerald, here we come!

They zoom off.